Lilly-Lolly Little-Legs

I wish I was bigger than my sister.
I hate it when she calls me
Lilly-lolly Little-legs.

Hey, Lilly-lolly Little-legs,
we need you to hold the rope.

No! Can't you see I'm climbing?

Hey, Lilly-lolly Little-legs,
we need you to get the ball.

6

No! Can't you see I'm building?

Hey, Lilly-lolly Little-legs,
we need you to get in here.

No! Can't you see I'm playing?

Hey, Lilly-lolly Little-legs,
we need you to be the horse.

No! Can't you see I'm thinking?

Hey, Lilly-lolly Little-legs,
we need you to hold the dog.

No! Can't you see I'm reading?

Hey, Lilly-lolly Little-legs,
we need you to climb up here.

Ooh yes! I'd like to do that.